IMPROVE YOUR GAME

100 Scrabble®
Puzzles

PAUL LAMFORD
& ALLAN SIMMONS

Chameleon Books

First published in 1999 by Chameleon Books,
an imprint of André Deutsch Ltd,
76 Dean Street London W1V 5HA
(www.vci.co.uk)

© Paul Lamford, Allan Simmons 1999

Scrabble® is a registered trademark of
J.W.Spear & Sons plc, Leicester LE3 2WT
and is used under licence from
Mattel Europa BV

The rights of Paul Lamford and Allan Simmons to be identified as the
Authors of this Work have been asserted by them in accordance
with the Copyright Design and Patents Act 1988

Typeset by Games and Pastimes Consultancy
8 Arbor Court London N16 0QU. Tel/Fax: (0181) 809 3063

British Library Cataloguing in Publication Data
Data available

ISBN 0 233 99715 6

Printed and bound in Great Britain by
MPG Books Ltd, Bodmin, Cornwall

Contents

Acknowledgements

The authors would like to thank Miranda Moore for invaluable assistance in checking all the material in this book and for proofreading and editing the text. However the authors take full responsibility for any errors and would welcome comments sent to them at gampas@aol.com

To Robbie, Carol and family (and the dogs)

Introduction

Scrabble® is one of the most popular word games in the world and over half of the households in the UK and USA own a set. It stems from a word game called Lexico, invented by Alfred Butts, became Criss-Crosswords when Jim Brunot became involved in 1939 and first commercially appeared as Scrabble in 1949. Since 1991 it has had a World Championship hosted by J W Spear & Sons plc, now part of Mattel.

The game is played on a 15 x 15 board with 100 lettered tiles. At the start of the game each player draws one tile randomly and the player with the letter nearest the start of the alphabet begins.

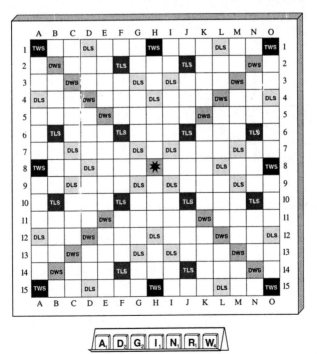

That player draws seven letters and places them in a rack as in the above diagram. On any turn a player may place one or more letters on the board to form a word or words horizontally or vertically only and adjacent to the words currently on the board.

The aim of the game is to place your letters on the board to score points, and it is almost exclusively played "head to head" between two players. The social game involving four players is never played competitively. The winner is the player who has scored the most points at the end of the game which is when one player has an empty rack and there are no more tiles in the bag from which letters are drawn or when each player has tiles but is unable to play or chooses not to play. At this point the total values of any tiles not played are deducted from a player's total score and added to the score of the opponent.

The letters have different values and the experienced Scrabble player will remember these together with the distribution of letters:

Letter	Value	Number	Letter	Value	Number
A	1	9	N	1	6
B	3	2	O	1	8
C	3	2	P	3	2
D	2	4	Q	10	1
E	1	12	R	1	6
F	4	2	S	1	4
G	2	3	Y	1	6
H	4	2	U	1	4
I	1	9	V	4	2
J	8	1	W	4	2
K	5	1	X	8	1
L	1	4	Y	4	2
M	3	2	Z	10	1

There are also two blanks which can be used to stand for any nominated letter but score zero. Near the end of a competitive game a player may perform what is called "tile-tracking" by counting the number of each letter played on the board to discover the remaining letters and there is considerable skill in the endgame phase.

On the board 60 squares are designated as bonus squares. There are four categories: double-letter squares, triple-letter squares, double-word squares and triple-word squares. In the diagrams these are indicated by DLS, TLS, DWS and TWS respectively. The central square is also a double-word square so that the score for the initial play is doubled.

From our previous diagram the player must make an initial play through this central square, or change one or more of his letters in which case the turn passes to the opponent. In our example, the player notices that he can use all seven letters in two ways, to make the word DRAWING or the word WARDING. Whichever he selects can commence on any square provided that one letter of the word is placed on the central square.

The better play is to make WARDING as the W, the highest-scoring tile he possesses, can thus be placed on the double-letter square D8 and it therefore scores 8 instead of 4. The score for the play is (8+1+1+2+1+1+2) = 16 x 2 = 32 plus a 50 bonus for using all seven letters on one turn, a total of 82 points. The move is notated as "WARDING at D8 across for 82 points", and this uniquely identifies the play. It is traditional to make the first move going across rather than down, but there is no requirement for this in the rules.

After the opening play the opponent must place one or more

letters on the board to make one or more words, or he may change as many tiles as he wishes for replacement tiles from the bag. Let us say that the opponent has the following rack:

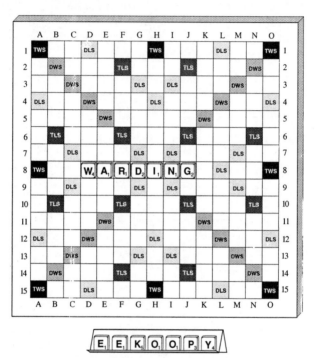

There are many words that he can play here. He could, for example, play KEG at J6 down. This would place the K on a triple-letter square and score (15+1+2) = 18 points. Another play would be WEEPY at D8 down. This scores (4+1+1+3+4) = 13 x 2 as the double-word score is covered, for a total of 26 points. He decides to play the word POKEY starting at A9 across and also making the words WE and AY leading to the diagram opposite. His score is then the total of the scores for each of these three words. POKEY scores (3+1+10+1+4) = 19; WE scores (4+1) = 5 and AY scores (1+4) = 5. The total score for this word is 29 points and this is the highest score he can achieve with these letters. This would be a poor play in tournament Scrabble because it provides the opponent access to the triple-word square next turn but this factor is ignored for the purpose of deciding on the highest-scoring play.

In the first half of this book you are presented with 50 problems in which the sole object is to make the highest-scoring play possible. These problems were all composed by Paul Lamford. Hints are given with each diagram and the more experienced player will prefer to tackle them without this help in the first instance. In the second half of the book there are 50 different challenges and these were all composed by Allan Simmons. Before you tackle any of the problems you will do well to familiarise yourself with the allowable two-letter words on the next page.

Two-letter word list

It is impossible to play a good game of Scrabble without being familiar with the two-letter words. The full list of allowable words is as follows (with one meaning as given in *The Chambers Dictionary*).

AA	a type of scoriaceous volcanic rock	EF	the letter F
AD	an advertisement	EH	an interjection used to request repetition
AE	a Scottish word for one	EL	the letter L
AH	an interjection expressing surprise	EM	the letter M
AI	the three-toed sloth	EN	the letter N
AM	the first person singular of the verb to be	ER	an interjection expressing hesitation
AN	the indefinite article	ES	the letter S
AR	the letter R	EX	the letter X
AS	an adverb	FA	a note in music
AT	a preposition	FY	an interjection denoting disapprobation
AW	an interjection expressing disgust	GI	a judo or karate costume
AX	an American form of axe	GO	to proceed
AY	an interjection	GU	a Shetland violin
BA	in ancient Egyptian religion, the soul	HA	an interjection of surprise or joy
BE	to live or exist	HE	the masculine pronoun
BI	short for bisexual	HI	an interjection calling attention
BO	an interjection used to startle	HO	an interjection expressing exultation
BY	a preposition	ID	a fish of the carp famiy
CH	an obsolete pronoun	IF	a conjunction
DA	a Burmese knife	IN	a preposition
DI	a plural of deus, a god	IO	an interjection of invocation
DO	to perform		
EA	running water	IS	the third person singular of the verb to be
EE	a Scottish word for an eye	IT	the neuter pronoun

JO	a Scottish loved one	OY	a Scottish word for a grandchild
KA	the spirit or soul		
KO	a Maori digging stick	PA	a word for a father
KY	a Scottish word for cows	PH	a measure of acidity or alkalinity
LA	a note in music		
LI	a Chinese unit of distance	PI	the Greek letter π
		PO	a contraction of chamberpot
LO	an archaic interjection meaning behold	QI	a Chinese life-force
MA	a contraction of mamma	RE	a note in music
ME	a personal pronoun	SH	an interjection requesting silence
MI	a note in music		
MO	an old word for more	SI	a note in music
MU	the Greek letter μ	SO	an adverb or conjunction
MY	a possessive adjective	ST	an interjection used to attract attention
NA	a Scottish form of no		
NE	an obsolete adverb meaning not	TA	an interjection used to express thanks
NO	not any or not one	TE	another spelling of TI
NU	the Greek letter ν	TI	a musical note
NY	an old spelling of nigh	TO	a preposition
OB	an objection	UG	to arouse loathing
OD	an archaic oath	UM	an interjection showing doubt
OE	another spelling of OY		
OF	a preposition	UN	a dialectic pronoun
OH	an interjection denoting surprise	UP	an adverb
		UR	an interjection showing a pause in thought
OI	an interjection used to attract attention		
		US	a pronoun
OM	a sacred syllable	UT	an old note in music
ON	a preposition	WE	a pronoun
OO	a Scottish form of we	WO	an old form of woe
OR	a conjunction	XI	the Greek letter ξ
OS	a bone	XU	the currency of Vietnam
OU	a Scottish interjection expressing concession	YE	an archaic pronoun
		YO	an interjection
OW	another spelling of OU	YU	precious jade
OX	an animal	ZO	a Himalayan animal

Highest Scores

1

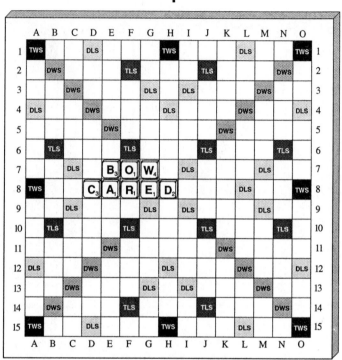

What's your highest-scoring play?

HINT
Look for an anagram of the seven letters on your
rack – then find somewhere to put it!

Solutions appear overleaf. The glossary at the end of the
book lists all unusual words which appear in the diagrams
or solutions.

2

What's your highest-scoring play?

Solutions appear overleaf. The glossary at the end of the
book lists all unusual words which appear in the diagrams
or solutions.

3

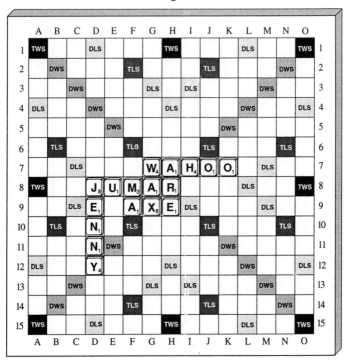

What's your highest-scoring play?

HINT
There is an anagram of the letters on your rack.
You have to find that and then somewhere to place it.

Solution to Puzzle 1

The highest-scoring play is to make EXHORTS, starting at C2 and
extending CARED to SCARED. This scores 95 points.

4

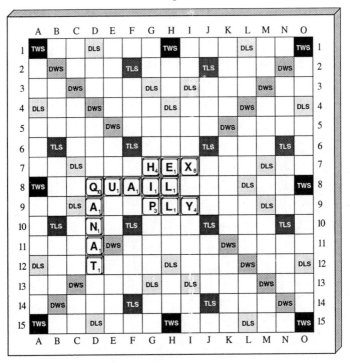

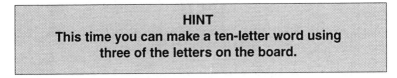

What's your highest-scoring play?

HINT
This time you can make a ten-letter word using
three of the letters on the board.

Solution to Puzzle 2

The highest-scoring play is to make MANICURE, starting at H2 and using the R of POKER. This scores 63 points

5

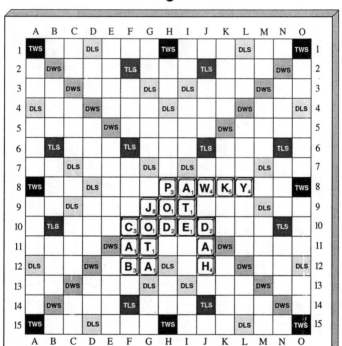

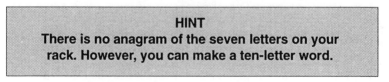

What's your highest-scoring play?

HINT
There is no anagram of the seven letters on your
rack. However, you can make a ten-letter word.

Solution to Puzzle 3

The highest-scoring play is to make YAMULKA, starting at G10
across and also making WAXY and AREA. This scores 89 points.

6

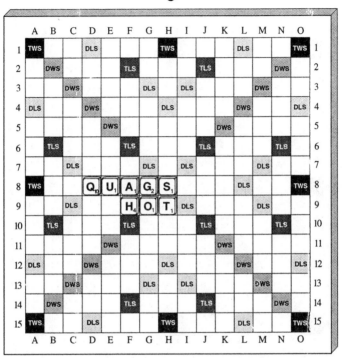

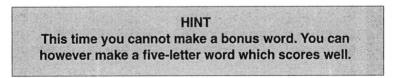

What's your highest-scoring play?

HINT
This time you cannot make a bonus word. You can however make a five-letter word which scores well.

Solution to Puzzle 4

The highest-scoring play is to make MIDSHIPMAN at G3 down, using the word HIP on the board. This scores 73 points.

7

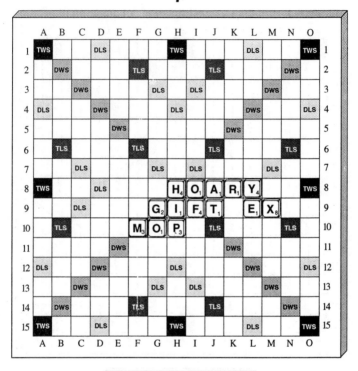

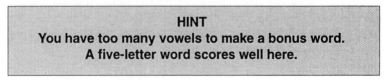

What's your highest-scoring play?

HINT
You have too many vowels to make a bonus word.
A five-letter word scores well here.

Solution to Puzzle 5

The highest-scoring play is to make USQUEBAUGH, starting at A12 across, around the BA already there and using the H at J12. This scores 104 points.

8

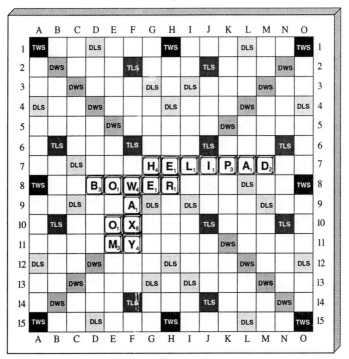

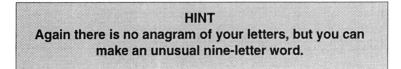

What's your highest-scoring play?

HINT
Again there is no anagram of your letters, but you can
make an unusual nine-letter word.

Solution to Puzzle 6
The highest-scoring play is to make GLYPH, starting at E7 across
and also making GU, LAH, YGO and PST. This scores 47 points.

9

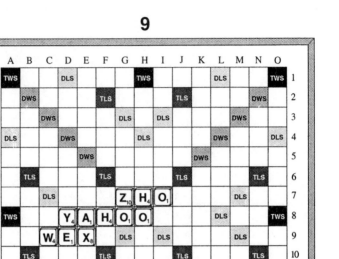

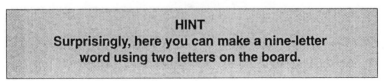

What's your highest-scoring play?

> ### HINT
> Surprisingly, here you can make a nine-letter
> word using two letters on the board.

Solution to Puzzle 7

The highest-scoring play is to make COOEE at H7 across, also
making CHIP, OOF, EAT, ER and EYE. This scores 37 points.

10

	A	B	C	D	E	F	G	H	I	J	K	L	M	N	O	
1	TWS			DLS				TWS				DLS			TWS	1
2		DWS				TLS				TLS				DWS		2
3			DWS				DLS		DLS				DWS			3
4	DLS			DWS				DLS				DWS			DLS	4
5					DWS						DWS					5
6		TLS				TLS				TLS				TLS		6
7				Z₁₀	Y₄	M₃	I₁	C₃		DLS			DLS			7
8	TWS			DLS				H₄	A₁	E₁		DLS			TWS	8
9			DLS				A₁	I₁	M₃				DLS			9
10		TLS				TLS	P₃	R₁	U₁	D₂	E₁			TLS		10
11				DWS							DWS					11
12	DLS			DWS				DLS				DWS			DLS	12
13			DWS				DLS		DLS				DWS			13
14		DWS				TLS				TLS				DWS		14
15	TWS			DLS				TWS				DLS			TWS	15
	A	B	C	D	E	F	G	H	I	J	K	L	M	N	O	

Rack: I₁ J₈ N₁ R₁ S₁ T₁ U₁

What's your highest-scoring play?

HINT
A spectacular 12-letter word is available here.
Can you find it?

Solution to Puzzle 8

The highest-scoring play is to make MYCORHIZA, starting at E11 across. This scores 106 points.

11

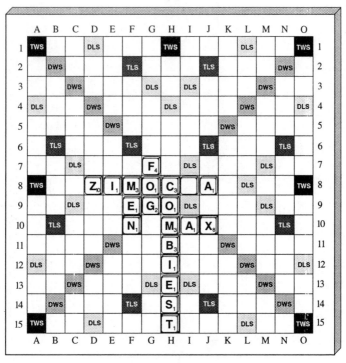

The blank in the diagram is a C

The blank in the diagram is a C

What's your highest-scoring play?

HINT
**This looks a terrible rack but you can use six of
your letters to make a seven-letter word.**

Solution to Puzzle 9

The highest-scoring play is to make HOBGOBLIN at H7 down
using the HO. This scores 110 points.

12

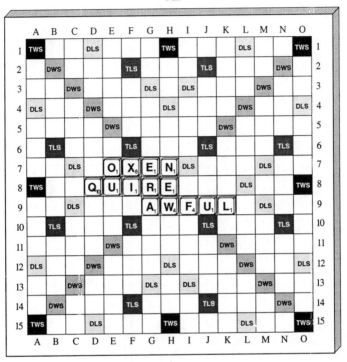

What's your highest-scoring play?

Solution to Puzzle 10

The highest-scoring play is to make JURISPRUDENT, starting at
B10 across around the word PRUDE. This scores 90 points.

13

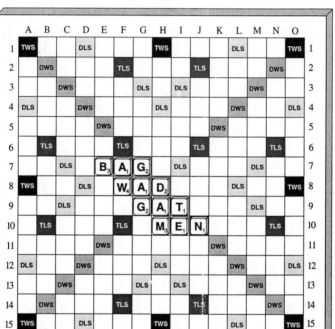

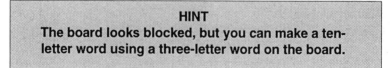

What's your highest-scoring play?

HINT
The board looks blocked, but you can make a ten-
letter word using a three-letter word on the board.

Solution to Puzzle 11

The highest-scoring play is to make OUABAIN, starting at E11
across and also making MENU, AA and XI. This scores 53 points.

14

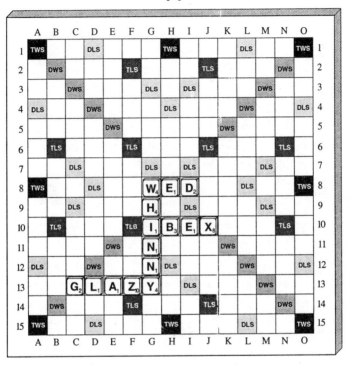

What's your highest-scoring play?

HINT
Clearly no bonus with this collection. Making a word
with the J is the best you can do.

Solution to Puzzle 12
The highest-scoring play is to make YOUNGTHLY, starting at E6
down around the OU already there. This scores 88 points.

15

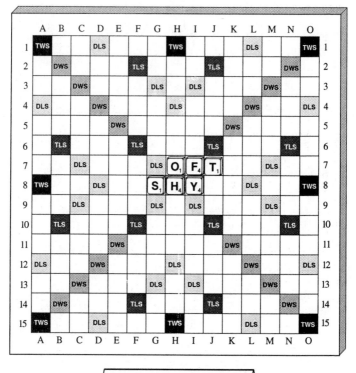

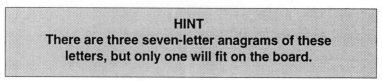

What's your highest-scoring play?

> **HINT**
> There are three seven-letter anagrams of these
> letters, but only one will fit on the board.

Solution to Puzzle 13

The highest-scoring play is to make ORNAMENTAL, starting at
D10 across and also making GAGA. This scores 70 points.

16

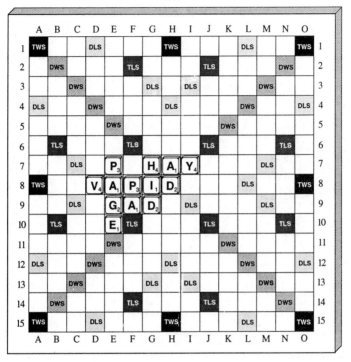

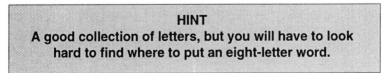

What's your highest-scoring play?

HINT
**A good collection of letters, but you will have to look
hard to find where to put an eight-letter word.**

Solution to Puzzle 14
The highest-scoring play is to make JIAO, starting at F6 down and
making AWED and OH. This scores 40 points.

17

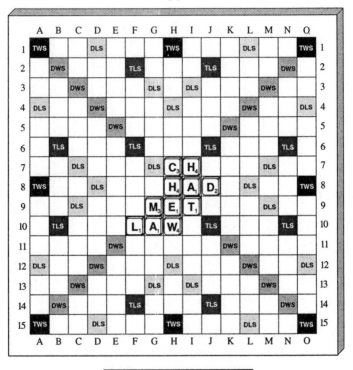

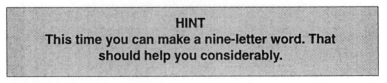

What's your highest-scoring play?

HINT
This time you can make a nine-letter word. That should help you considerably.

Solution to Puzzle 15
The highest-scoring play is to make RIBLETS, starting at B6 across and also making SOH. This scores 69 points.

18

The blank in the diagram is an A

What's your highest-scoring play?

HINT
A vowel-heavy rack again. How do you use several of
them to score well?

Solution to Puzzle 16
The highest-scoring play is to make SOUVENIR, starting at D5
down and also making UP, EGAD, and NE. This scores 84 points.

19

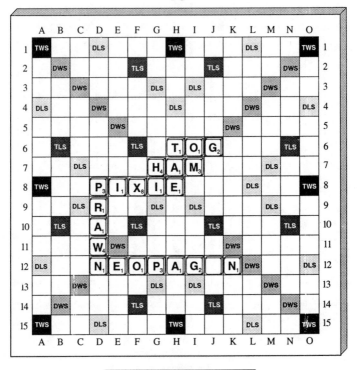

The blank in the diagram is an A

What's your highest-scoring play?

Solution to Puzzle 17
The highest-scoring play is to make SCHILLING starting at F7 across and also making ID. This scores 70 points.

20

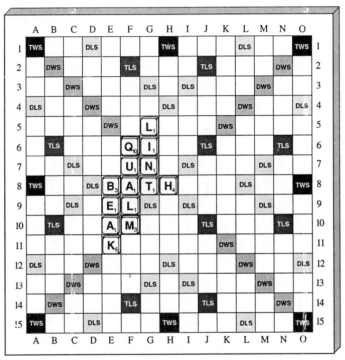

You have a blank on your rack

What's your highest-scoring play?

HINT
A spectacular 11-letter word is available here
using one of the words on the board.

Solution to Puzzle 18

The highest-scoring play is to make HOODOO at E7 across, also making OPALS, DAN and OYE. This scores 31 points.

21

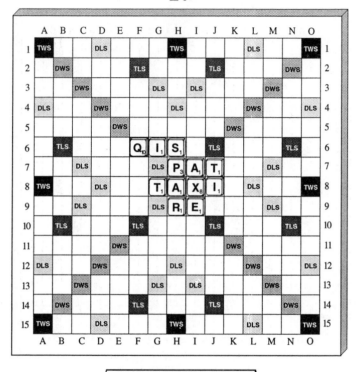

What's your highest-scoring play?

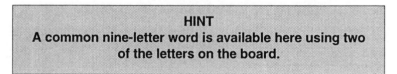

HINT
A common nine-letter word is available here using two
of the letters on the board.

Solution to Puzzle 19

The highest-scoring play is to make AQUALUNG, starting at K6
down and also making TOGA. This scores 91 points.

22

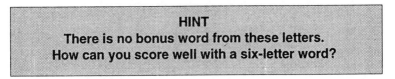

What's your highest-scoring play?

HINT
There is no bonus word from these letters.
How can you score well with a six-letter word?

Solution to Puzzle 20

The highest-scoring play is to make BATHMITZVAH by using the blank as a V and adding your letters to BATH at E8 across. This scores a massive 167 points.

23

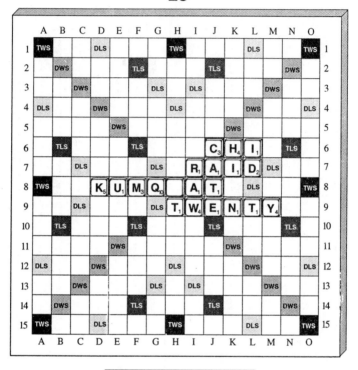

The blank in the diagram is a U

What's your highest-scoring play?

HINT
A spectacular but well-known ten-letter word slots in neatly here. Can you find it?

Solution to Puzzle 21

The highest-scoring play is to make FIREPLACE, starting at F9 across and also making TI and TIP. This scores 78 points.

24

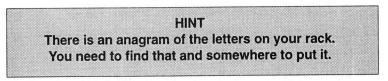

What's your highest-scoring play?

HINT
There is an anagram of the letters on your rack.
You need to find that and somewhere to put it.

Solution to Puzzle 22

The highest-scoring play is to make WRIGHT starting at H6 across and also making WHAT, RAX and ID. This scores 40 points.

25

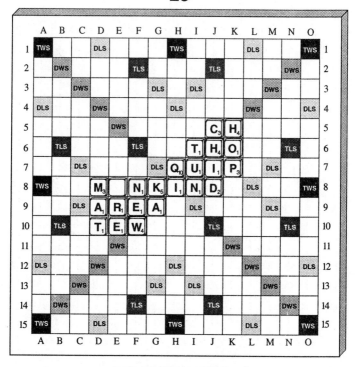

The blank in the diagram is an A

What's your highest-scoring play?

HINT
A vowel-heavy rack here. How do you get rid of
several of them and score well?

Solution to Puzzle 23

The highest-scoring play is to make GRANDCHILD, starting at E6
across and also making DRAW. This scores 82 points.

26

The blank in the diagram is an E

What's your highest-scoring play?

HINT
On this wide-open board you can make a nine-letter word using two of the letters already there.

Solution to Puzzle 24

The highest-scoring play is to make AMPUTEE, starting at G6 across and making ABED, MARE, PI and UT. This scores 84 points.

27

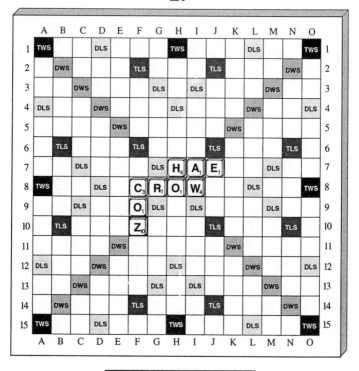

What's your highest-scoring play?

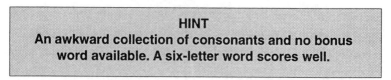

HINT
An awkward collection of consonants and no bonus
word available. A six-letter word scores well.

Solution to Puzzle 25
The highest-scoring play is to make EUOI, starting at L5 down and
making CHE, THOU and QUIPO. This scores 36 points.

28

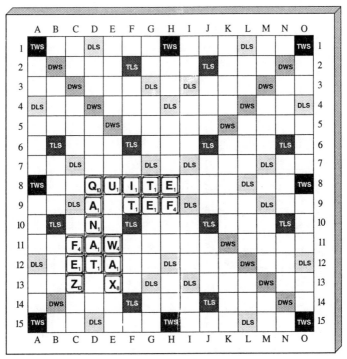

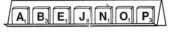

What's your highest-scoring play?

HINT
No bonus word here, but you can use the J
to make a reasonable score.

Solution to Puzzle 26

The highest-scoring play is to make GUITARIST, starting at D11 across. This scores 90 points.

29

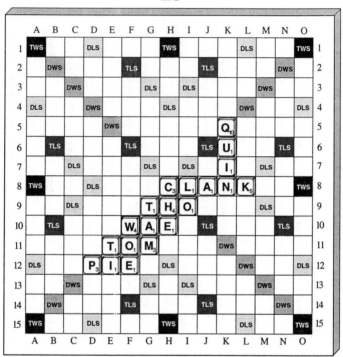

What's your highest-scoring play?

Solution to Puzzle 27

The highest-scoring play is to make KVETCH starting at E6 across,
also making THO, CAW and HE. This scores 61 points.

30

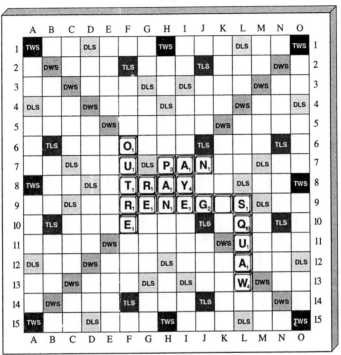

The blank in the diagram is an E

What's your highest-scoring play?

HINT
A spectacular 11-letter word is available here,
using four of the tiles on the board.

Solution to Puzzle 28

The highest-scoring play is to make BANJO, starting at F7 across
and also making BIT, ATE and NEF. This scores 38 points.

31

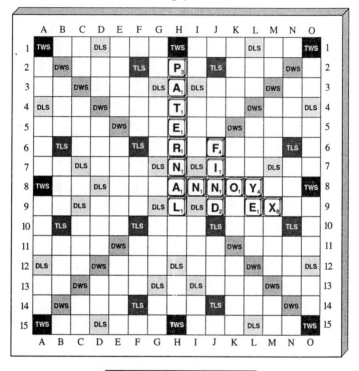

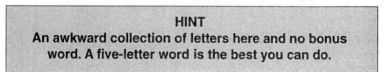

What's your highest-scoring play?

HINT
An awkward collection of letters here and no bonus
word. A five-letter word is the best you can do.

Solution to Puzzle 29

The highest-scoring play is to make TOMFOOLERY, starting at
E11 across and also making CHEF. This scores 98 points.

32

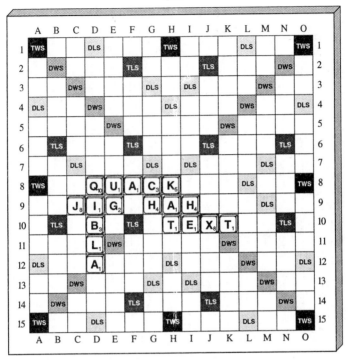

What's your highest-scoring play?

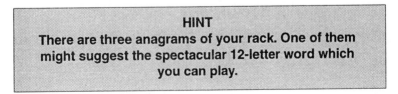

HINT
There are three anagrams of your rack. One of them
might suggest the spectacular 12-letter word which
you can play.

Solution to Puzzle 30

The highest-scoring play is to make COMEUPPANCE, starting at
B7 across and also making PRE. This scores 83 points.

33

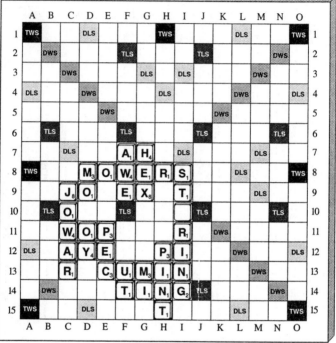

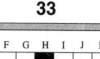

The blank in the diagram is an O

What's your highest-scoring play?

HINT
A clever 11-letter word slots in somewhere, but you
need to know a couple of rare words.

Solution to Puzzle 31

The highest-scoring play is to make UHURU, starting at G2 down
and also making UP, HA, UT, RE and UR. This scores 31 points.

34

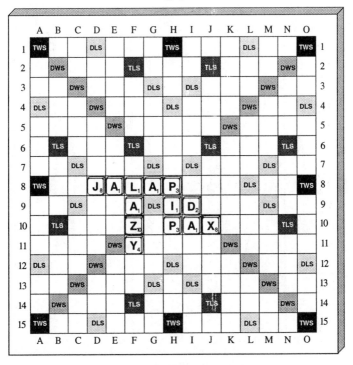

What's your highest-scoring play?

Solution to Puzzle 32
The highest-scoring play is to make QUACKSALVING, starting at
D8 across and also making SHE. This scores 161 points.

35

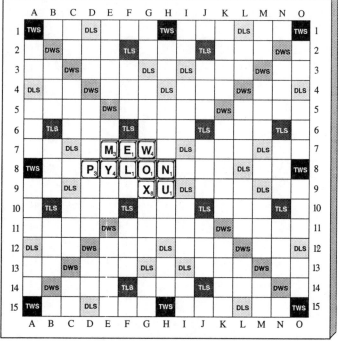

What's your highest-scoring play?

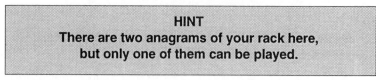

HINT
There are two anagrams of your rack here,
but only one of them can be played.

Solution to Puzzle 33
The highest-scoring play is to make NIGHTINGALE, starting at B14 across and also making JOWARI and PECH. This scores 113 points.

36

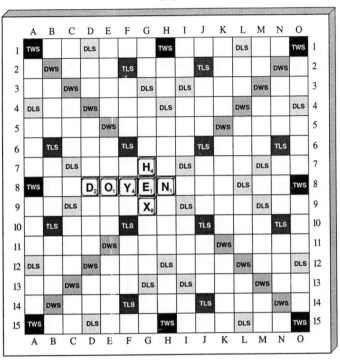

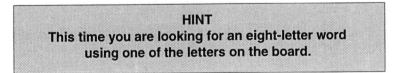

What's your highest-scoring play?

HINT
This time you are looking for an eight-letter word
using one of the letters on the board.

Solution to Puzzle 34

The highest-scoring play is to make ILIUM, starting at H11 across
and also making PIPI, DAL and XI. This scores 35 points.

37

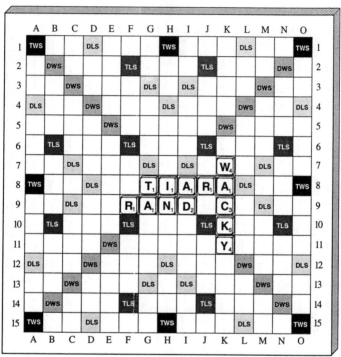

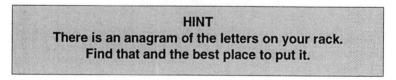

What's your highest-scoring play?

HINT
There is an anagram of the letters on your rack.
Find that and the best place to put it.

Solution to Puzzle 35
The highest-scoring play is to make BRIGADE, starting at H10 across and also making NUB. This scores 70 points.

38

What's your highest-scoring play?

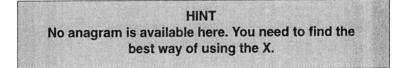

HINT
No anagram is available here. You need to find the
best way of using the X.

Solution to Puzzle 36

The highest-scoring play is to make HANDCUFF, starting at D5
down. This scores 90 points.

39

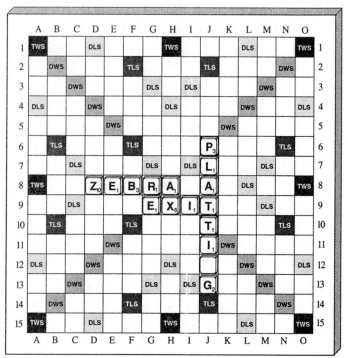

The blank in the diagram is an N

What's your highest-scoring play?

HINT
Here you need to find an eight-letter word using one of
the letters on the board.

Solution to Puzzle 37

The highest-scoring play is to make NEWSBOY, starting at E5 down
and also making BRAND. This scores 118 points.

40

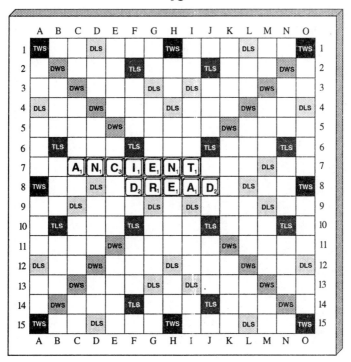

E₁ E₁ G₂ I₁ J₈ R₁ O₁

What's your highest-scoring play?

HINT
No bonus word is available, but what is the best use
you can make of the J?

Solution to Puzzle 38
The highest-scoring play is to make TAXED, starting at D10 across
and also making ERA, BOX and BEE. This scores 65 points.

41

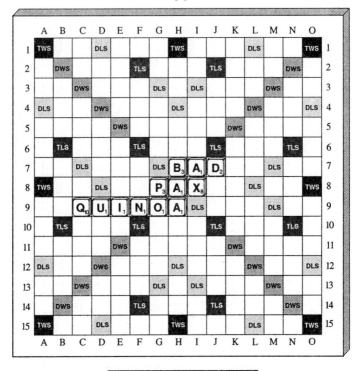

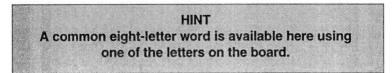

What's your highest-scoring play?

> **HINT**
> A common eight-letter word is available here using
> one of the letters on the board.

Solution to Puzzle 39

The highest-scoring play is to make BACHELOR, starting at E4
down. This scores 110 points.

42

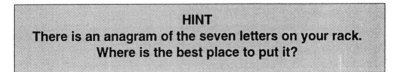

What's your highest-scoring play?

HINT
There is an anagram of the seven letters on your rack.
Where is the best place to put it?

Solution to Puzzle 40

The highest-scoring play is to make REJIG starting at G9 across and also making ERR, NEE, TAJ and DI. This scores 50 points.

43

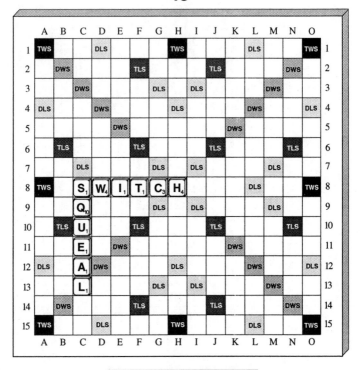

What's your highest-scoring play?

HINT
No anagram of your letters here. This time you have
to make best use of the X.

Solution to Puzzle 41
The highest-scoring play is to make ARMCHAIR, starting at E3
down. This scores 80 points.

44

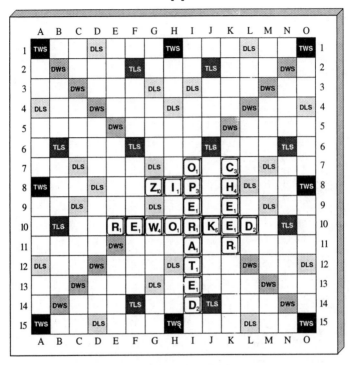

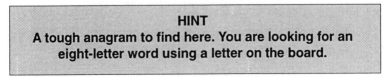

What's your highest-scoring play?

HINT
A tough anagram to find here. You are looking for an
eight-letter word using a letter on the board.

Solution to Puzzle 42

The highest-scoring play is to make HANDSET, starting at F5 down
and also making NOB, DROVE and SEX. This scores 89 points.

45

What's your highest-scoring play?

HINT
There is an anagram of the seven letters on your rack.
However the highest score is achieved by making
a nine-letter word using two letters on the board.

Solution to Puzzle 43
The highest-scoring play is to make XEBEC, starting at B10 down
and also making XU, EE, BA and EL. This scores 97 points.

46

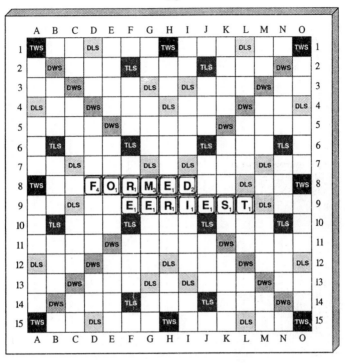

What's your highest-scoring play?

Solution to Puzzle 44

The highest-scoring play is to make BIRIYANI, starting at H1 down
and also making NO. This scores 94 points.

47

	A	B	C	D	E	F	G	H	I	J	K	L	M	N	O	
1	TWS			DLS				TWS				DLS			TWS	1
2		DWS			S₁	TLS				TLS				DWS		2
3			DWS		O₁		DLS		DLS				DWS			3
4	DLS			DWS	M₃			DLS				DWS			DLS	4
5					B₃						DWS					5
6		TLS			R₁	TLS				TLS				TLS		6
7			DLS				DLS		DLS				DLS			7
8	TWS			C₃	R₁	Y₄	P₃	T₁				DLS			TWS	8
9			DLS	H₄	O₁		DLS		DLS				DLS			9
10		TLS		I₁		TLS				TLS				TLS		10
11				M₃	DWS						DWS					11
12	DLS			E₁				DLS				DWS			DLS	12
13			DWS				DLS		DLS				DWS			13
14		DWS				TLS				TLS				DWS		14
15	TWS			DLS				TWS				DLS			TWS	15
	A	B	C	D	E	F	G	H	I	J	K	L	M	N	O	

Rack: A₁ E₁ H₄ I₁ O₁ O₁ Z₁₀

The blank in the diagram is an E

What's your highest-scoring play?

HINT
There is no bonus word from this rack. This time you
need to make best use of the Z.

Solution to Puzzle 45

The highest-scoring play is to make TREACHERY at H7 down for
113 points.

48

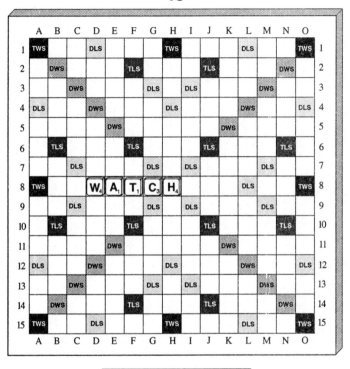

A₁ C₃ D₂ E₁ G₂ M₃ R₁

What's your highest-scoring play?

HINT
An eight-letter word for you to find here.
This is harder than it appears.

Solution to Puzzle 46

The highest-scoring play is to make PHLEGM, starting at E10 across and also making REH, MEL, ERE, DIG and EM. This scores 65 points.

49

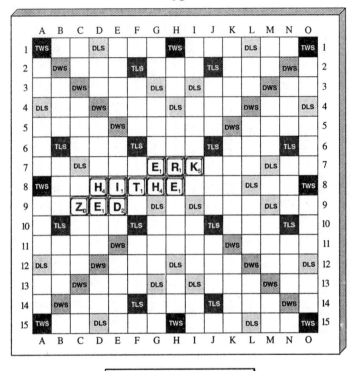

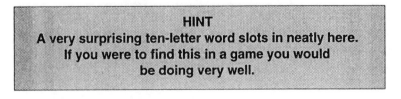

What's your highest-scoring play?

HINT
A very surprising ten-letter word slots in neatly here.
If you were to find this in a game you would
be doing very well.

Solution to Puzzle 47
The highest-scoring play is to make ZOOEA, starting at C9 down
and also making ZHO, OI, OM, EM and AE. This scores 81 points.

50

What's your highest-scoring play?

HINT
This time you need to make an eight-letter word using
one of the letters on the board.

Solution to Puzzle 48

The highest-scoring play is to make DECAGRAM, starting at E5 down. This scores 106 points.

Target Practice

The target score challenges

In the next 50 positions, all of which were composed by Allan Simmons, you will usually be asked to achieve a target score, to find a seven-letter anagram or to use certain tiles. The requirements are always stated in the grey box below the diagram.

Usually the solutions are fairly common words such that you shouldn't need to consult a dictionary. However, familiarity with the allowable two-letter words on pages 10-11 will be helpful occasionally.

The solutions to the target score challenges are often well-hidden and may utilise several of the existing letters on the board.

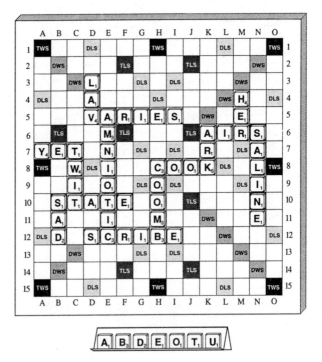

For example, in the above position the reader may be invited to find a play that scores exactly 51 points and a play that scores just over 51 points. In our example the play that scores 51 points is COOKABLE at H8 across and the play that just exceeds this target score is OUTWITTED at C5 down for 57 points. Both these plays have been highlighted in the following diagram:

	A	B	C	D	E	F	G	H	I	J	K	L	M	N	O	
1	TWS			DLS				TWS				DLS			TWS	1
2		DWS				TLS				TLS				DWS		2
3			DWS	L₁			DLS		DLS				DWS			3
4	DLS			A₁				DLS				DWS	H₄		DLS	4
5			O₁	V₄	A₁	R₁	I₁	E₁	S₁		DWS		E₁			5
6		TLS	U₁		M₃	TLS				TLS	A₁	I₁	R₁	S₁		6
7	Y₄	E₁	T₁		N₁		DLS		DLS		R₁		DLS	A₁		7
8	TWS		W₄	DLS	I₁			C₃	O₁	O₁	K₅	A₁	B₃	L₁	E₁	8
9			I₁		O₁		DLS	O₁	DLS				DLS	I₁		9
10		S₁	T₁	A₁	T₁	E₁		O₁		TLS				N₁		10
11		A₁	T₁		I₁			M₃			DWS		E₁			11
12	DLS	D₂	E₁	S₁	C₃	R₁	I₁	B₃	E₁			DWS			DLS	12
13			D₂				DLS		DLS				DWS			13
14		DWS				TLS				TLS				DWS		14
15	TWS			DLS				TWS				DLS			TWS	15
	A	B	C	D	E	F	G	H	I	J	K	L	M	N	O	

Some of the puzzles incorporate some very tempting solutions that are agonisingly close to the target. These are designed to frustrate! You need to look harder if you have found an apparent solution just a point or so less than the target. The play that scores just above the target will always score no more than an additional nine points.

Each puzzle includes at least one unusual word for added interest. Such words will hardly ever play a part in the solution and definitions of all these words are given in the glossary on page 119.

51

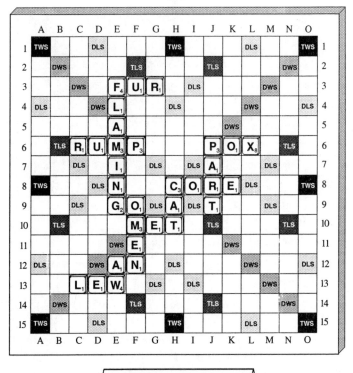

Your target score is 48

Can you find a play that scores exactly 48?
Can you find a play that scores just over 48?
Without using the Y can you score exactly 36?

Solution to Puzzle 49

The highest-scoring play is to make SAUERKRAUT, starting at D7
across and also making SHE, AID and UT. This scores 77 points.

52

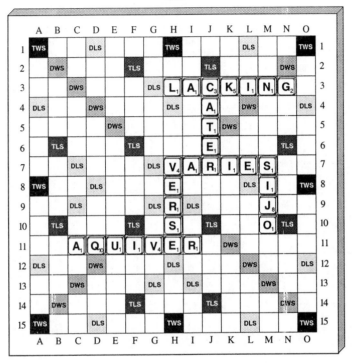

Your target score is 43

Can you find a play that scores exactly 43?
Can you find a play that scores just over 43?
What is the highest score you can get for
playing through the A of AQUIVER?

Solution to Puzzle 50

The highest-scoring play is to make FLAGPOLE, starting at F6
across. This scores 78 points.

53

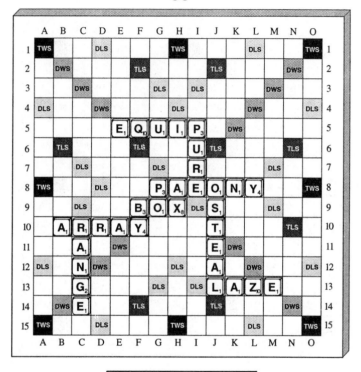

Your target score is 58

Can you find a play that scores exactly 58?
Can you find a seven-letter word with your tiles
and find somewhere to play it on the above board?

Solution to Puzzle 51

CATEGORY at H8 down scores 48 points. GEOMETRY at C10 across scores 54 points. TOERAG at B1 down scores 36 points.

54

	A	B	C	D	E	F	G	H	I	J	K	L	M	N	O	
1	TWS			DLS				TWS				DLS			TWS	1
2		DWS				TLS	E₁			TLS				DWS		2
3			DWS				X₈	Y₄	S₁	T₁	I₁		DWS			3
4	DLS			DWS			E₁	DLS				DWS			DLS	4
5				DWS			C₃				DWS					5
6	W₄	A₁	N₁	D₂	TLS	U₁			TLS				TLS			6
7			DLS		A₁		T₁		DLS			DLS				7
8	TWS			DLS	C₃	L₁	E₁	F₄	T₁			DLS			TWS	8
9		DLS		E₁		DLS	L₁	O₁	N₁	G₂		DLS				9
10		TLS			TLS		A₁		TLS	E₁			TLS			10
11				DWS			M₃			N₁						11
12	DLS			DWS			E₁			T₁	DWS			DLS		12
13			DWS			DLS		DLS				DWS				13
14		DWS			TLS				TLS				DWS			14
15	TWS			DLS			TWS				DLS			TWS		15
	A	B	C	D	E	F	G	H	I	J	K	L	M	N	O	

Rack: A₁ D₂ G₂ H₄ R₁ T₁ Y₄

Your target score is 38

Can you find a play that scores exactly 38?
What is the highest score you can get for playing
the letters AGRTY only?

Solution to Puzzle 52

BINGO at G3 down scores 43 points. OVERSEEING at H6 down scores 45 points. BEANO at C9 down scores 20 points.

55

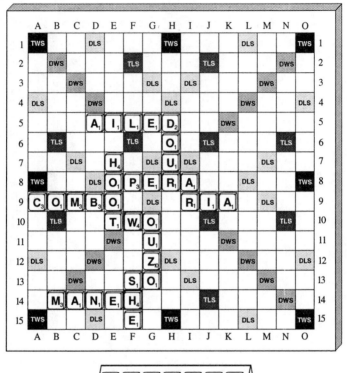

**Can you find a seven-letter anagram with the above tiles
and find somewhere to play it on the above board?
What is the highest score you can get for playing
through the square A8?**

Solution to Puzzle 53

HEARTEN at E11 across scores 58 points. EARTHEN at A15 across
scores 90 points

56

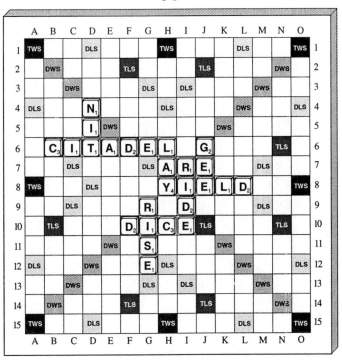

Your target score is 39

Can you find a play that scores exactly 39?
Can you find a play that scores just over 39?
Can you play three tiles only to score exactly 28?

Solution to Puzzle 54

HYDRANT at D1 down scores 38 points. GYRATE at B2 across scores 24 points.

57

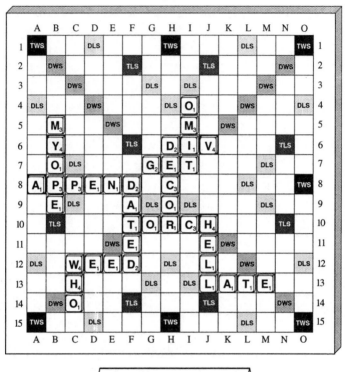

Can you play only four tiles to score exactly 60?
Can you find a seven-letter word anagram with the above
tiles and find three places to play it on the board?

Solution to Puzzle 55

ONBOARD at H4 across scores 79 points. BRONCO at 5A down
scores 30 points.

58

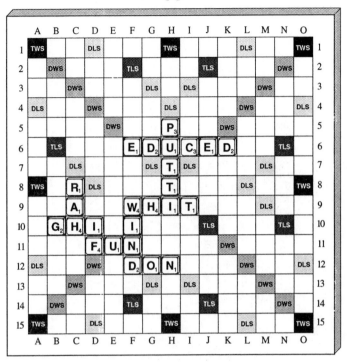

Your target score is 34

Can you find a play that scores exactly 34?
Can you find a play that scores just over 34?

Solution to Puzzle 56

UNDERLAY at H1 down scores 39 points. JAUNDICED at B10 across scores 40 points. RAJ at F12 down scores 28 points.

59

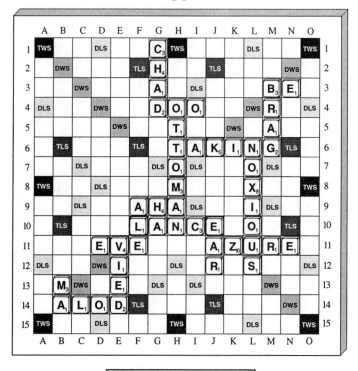

Your target score is 45

Can you find a play that scores exactly 45?
Can you find a play that scores just over 45?
Can you play only four tiles to score exactly 42?

Solution to Puzzle 57

BORAX at B14 across scores 60 points. GEARBOX at A15 across scores 114 points, at E14 across it scores 90 points and at N7 across it scores 81 points.

60

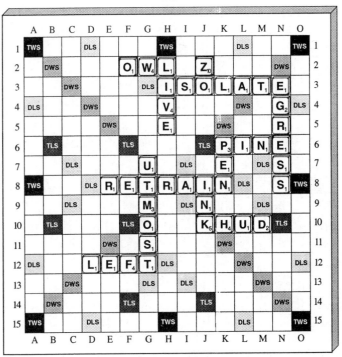

Your target score is 37

Can you find a play that scores exactly 37?
Can you find a play that scores just over 37?
What is the highest score you can get for playing
the letters C, P and U only?

Solution to Puzzle 58

EDIFICE at D8 down scores 34 points. FUNGICIDE at D11 across
scores 37 points.

61

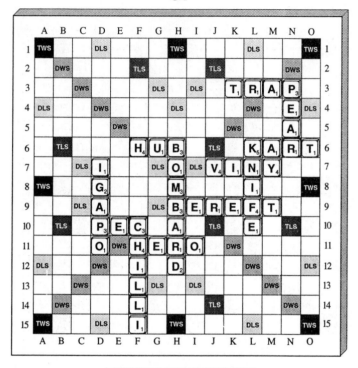

Your target score is 45

Can you find a play that scores exactly 45?
What is the highest score you can get for
playing the L only?

Solution to Puzzle 59

BIVOUAC at A1 across scores 45 points. JUBILANCE at B10 across
scores 49 points. OUIJA at K4 down scores 42 points.

62

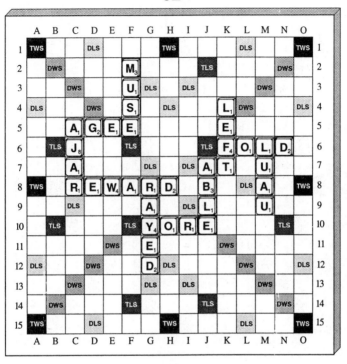

Your target score is 46

Can you find a play that scores exactly 46?
Can you play just six tiles to score exactly 29?

Solution to Puzzle 60

RECOUP at A1 across scores 37 points. PORCUPINE at F6 across scores 40 points. CUP at C12 down scores 24 points.

63

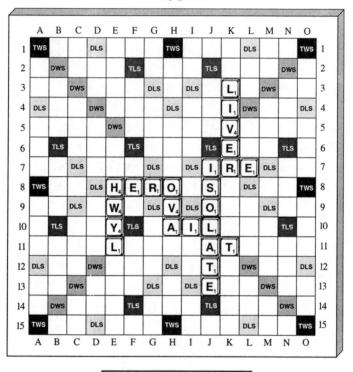

Your target score is 30

Can you find a play that scores exactly 30?
Can you find a play that scores just over 30?
What is the highest score you can get involving the P?

Solution to Puzzle 61

MOLLUSC at C13 across scores 45 points. VINYL at J7 across scores 18 points.

64

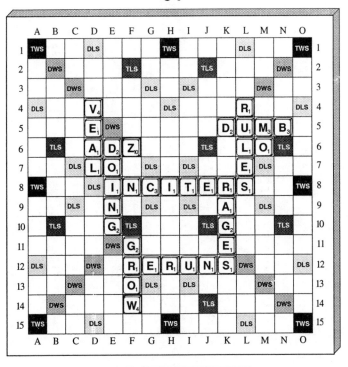

Can you find a seven-letter anagram with the above
tiles and find three places to play it on the board?
What is the highest score you can get for
playing only two letters?

Solution to Puzzle 62

FJORDS at B6 across scores 46 points. SCARFED at B11 across
scores 29 points.

65

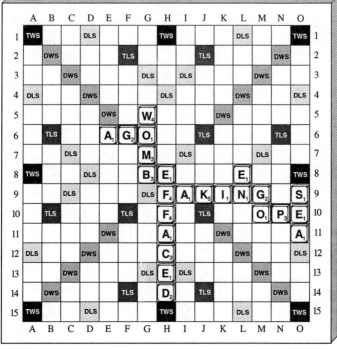

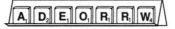

Your target score is 46

Can you find a play that scores exactly 46?
Can you find a play that scores just over 46?

Solution to Puzzle 63

BOTANY at H12 across scores 30 points. BONFIRE at F7 across
scores 31 points. PYLON at I3 across or PEONY at I13 across
both score 26 points.

66

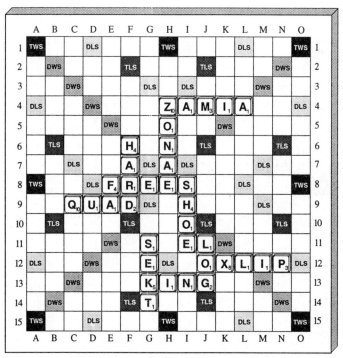

Your target score is 40

**Can you find a play that scores exactly 40?
What is the highest score you can get for playing
through the square F13?**

Solution to Puzzle 64

UNIFORM can be played at O1 down for 108 points, at E15 across
for 95 points or at D3 across for 75 points. FORERUNS at D12
scores 22 points.

67

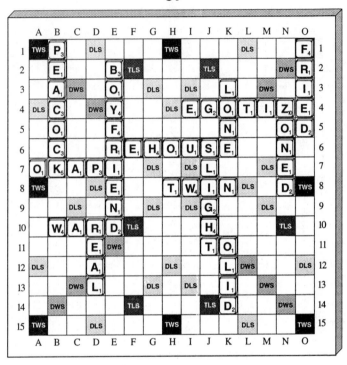

Can you play only five tiles to score over 40?
Can you find a seven-letter word anagram of the above
tiles and find somewhere to play it on the board?

Solution to Puzzle 65

WORRIED at K5 down scores 46 points. WARDROBE at A8 across
scores 48 points.

68

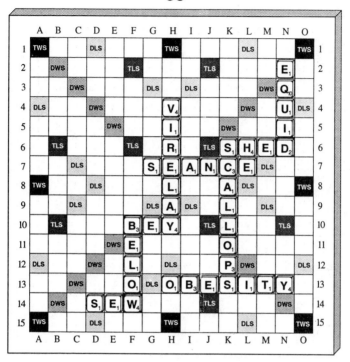

Your target score is 45

Can you find a play that scores exactly 45?
What is the highest score you can get using
only vowels from your rack?

Solution to Puzzle 66

WATERLOG at J6 down scores 40 points. HARDWARE at F6 down
scores 37 points.

69

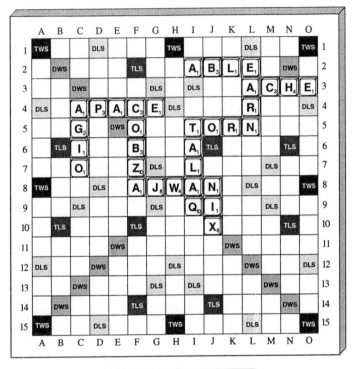

Your target score is 44

Can you find a play which scores exacly 44?
Can you find a play that scores just over 44?
Can you play a four-letter word to score exactly
38 in three different places?

Solution to Puzzle 67

FROGMAN at E5 across scores 41 points. EMBARGO at C14
across scores 71 points.

70

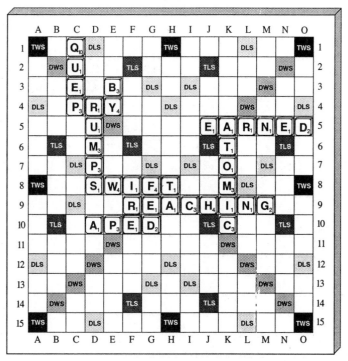

Your target score is 40

Can you find a play that scores 40 using exactly six tiles?
There are several seven-letter words with the above tiles;
which is the only one that is playable?

Solution to Puzzle 68

HOUSEWIFE at A14 across scores 45 points. OE at J5 across
scores 30 points.

71

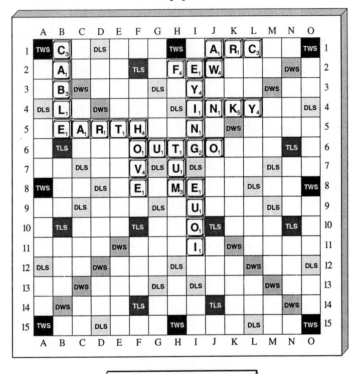

Your tiles: A₁ D₂ E₁ H₄ I₁ R₁ T₁

Your target score is 43

Can you find a play that scores exactly 43?
Can you play just two tiles to score exactly 27?

Solution to Puzzle 69

MYRRH at E1 across scores 44 points. RHYTHM at N2 down
scores 50 points. HYMN scores 38 points at F1 across, I11 across
or B6 down.

72

	A	B	C	D	E	F	G	H	I	J	K	L	M	N	O	
1	TWS			DLS				TWS				DLS			TWS	1
2		A₁	D₂	O₁		TLS	F₄			TLS				DWS		2
3			O₁	X₈	I₁	D₂	I₁	Z₁₀	E₁			P₃	DWS			3
4	DLS			DWS			L₁	DLS			Q₁₀	U₁	I₁	P₃	DLS	4
5				DWS			E₁				DWS	N₁		I₁		5
6		TLS				TLS	D₂	A₁	D₂	O₁		I₁		L₁		6
7			DLS			DLS	T₁	DLS				S₁	DLS	I₁		7
8	TWS			DLS			T₁	E₁	N₁	T₁	H₄			TWS		8
9			DLS			DLS	I₁	DLS					DLS			9
10		TLS				L₁	A₁	C₃	E₁	S₁				TLS		10
11				DWS					I₁	DWS						11
12	DLS			DWS			V₄	A₁	N₁		DWS			DLS		12
13			DWS			DLS	E₁	DLS	G₂			DWS				13
14		DWS		H₄	O₁	S₁	T₁		TLS				DWS			14
15	TWS			DLS			TWS				DLS			TWS		15
	A	B	C	D	E	F	G	H	I	J	K	L	M	N	O	

B₃ C₃ E₁ E₁ G₂ I₁ R₁

Your target score is 56

Can you find a play that scores exactly 56?
Find a play that scores just over 56 without using the B.
Can you find a seven-letter word with the above tiles and
find somewhere to play it on the board?

Solution to Puzzle 70

MIDNIGHT at D6 across scores 40 points. The anagrams are
DISHING, HIDINGS and SHINDIG. Only SHINDIG is playable at
B4 down and scores 77 points.

73

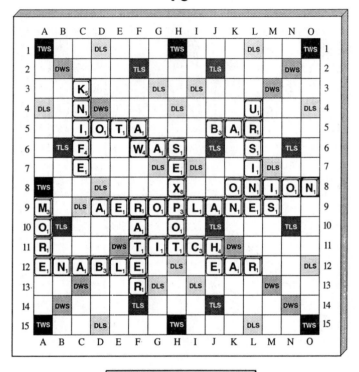

Your target score is 54

Can you find a play which scores exactly 54?
What is the lowest score you can get for
playing only six tiles?

Solution to Puzzle 71

BIRTHDAY at B3 across scores 43 points. DATUM at H4 down
scores 27 points.

74

Rack: A A E H R R T

Your target score is 42

Can you find a play which scores exactly 42?
What is the highest score you can get for playing
through square D3 without using the H?

Solution to Puzzle 72

RECOGNISING at J3 down scores 56 points. GRIEVANCE at D12
down scores 60 points. ICEBERG at D8 down scores 85 points.

75

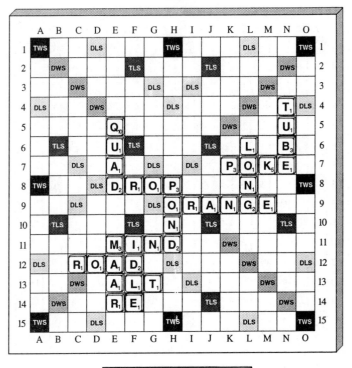

Your target score is 26

Can you find a play that scores exactly 26?
Can you find a play that scores just over 26?

Solution to Puzzle 73
SPHINX at C8 across scores 54 points. SIPHON at F14 across
scores just 23 points.

76

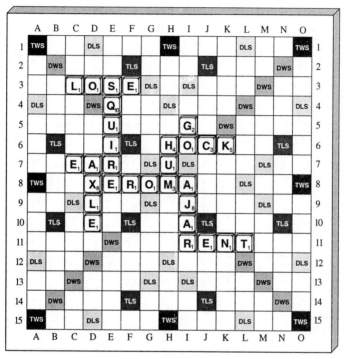

Your target score is 39

Can you find a play that scores exactly 39?
What is the highest score you can get
without using the Z?

Solution to Puzzle 74

CATARRH at N4 down scores 42 points. ERRATA at B3 across
scores 24 points.

77

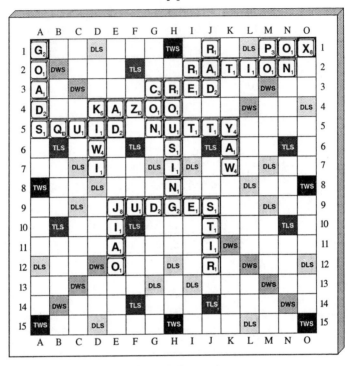

Your target score is 38

Can you find a play that scores exactly 38?
Can you find an eight-letter word with the above
tiles and using a letter on the board?

Solution to Puzzle 75

MINDFUL at E11 across scores 26 points. UNLAWFUL at E6 across
scores 28 points.

78

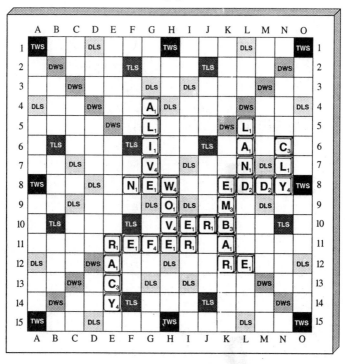

Your target score is 38

Can you find a play that scores exactly 38 points?
Can you find a play that scores just over 38 points?

Solution to Puzzle 76

ECZEMA at D10 across scores 39 points. EMU at E2 across scores 37 points.

79

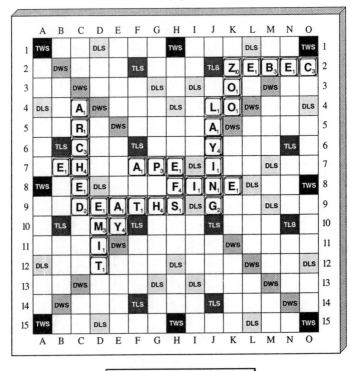

Your target score is 34

Can you find a play that scores exactly 34 points?
Can you find a play that scores just over 34 points?

Solution to Puzzle 77

ORIGAMI at A2 across scores 38 points. ADMIRING at G8 down using the D scores 65 points.

80

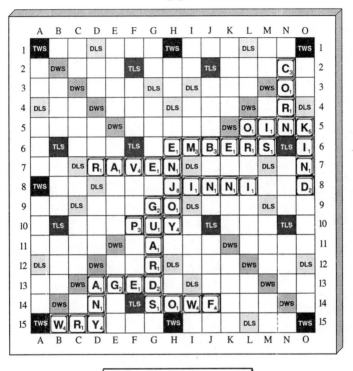

Can you find a seven-letter anagram with the above
tiles and in how many places can you play it?
What is the highest score you can get
without playing the B?

Solution to Puzzle 78

OKAPI at J13 across scores 38 points. RIVERBANK at F10 across
scores 39 points.

81

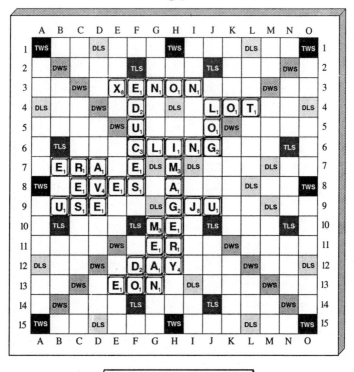

Your target score is 47

Can you find a play that scores exactly 47?
Can you find a play that scores just over 47?
Can you play just five tiles to score exactly 45?

Solution to Puzzle 79
DOORWAY at E4 down scores 34 points. CORDUROY at C6 across
scores 36 points.

82

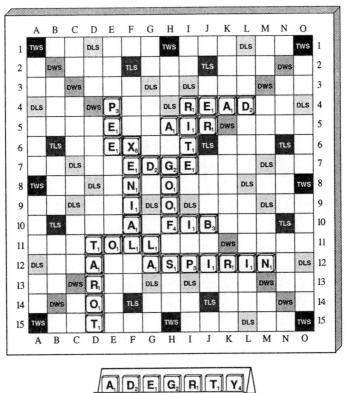

Can you find two seven-letter anagrams with the above
tiles and find two places to play each of them?

Solution to Puzzle 80

ALGEBRA can be played at A9 down for 113 points, at H1 across
for 96 points, at N8 down for 81 points and at C5 down for 77
points. GALA at A12 down scores 51 points.

83

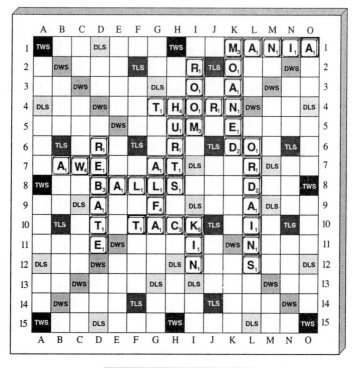

Your target score is 49

> Can you find a play that scores exactly 49?
> Can you find a play that scores just over 49?
> Can you play just five tiles to score exactly 38?

Solution to Puzzle 81

HYBRID at A4 across scores 47 points. BICYCLING at B6 across scores 48 points. BIRTHDAY at A12 across scores 45 points.

84

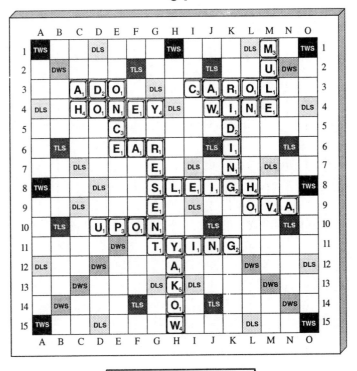

Can you find a seven-letter anagram of the above
tiles and find somewhere to play it on the board?
Can you score over 40 by playing just three tiles?

Solution to Puzzle 82

TRAGEDY can be played at N9 down for 89 points and at A3 across
for 88 points. GYRATED can be played at C8 down for 96 points
and at M3 down for 89 points.

85

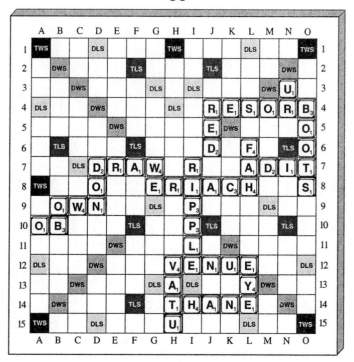

Your target score is 44

Can you find a play that scores exactly 44?
Can you find a play that scores just over 44?
Can you play four tiles to score exactly 36
without using the Z?

Solution to Puzzle 83

EYEBALLS at A8 across scores 49 points. YOGHURTS at H1 down
scores 50 points. GEODE at A12 across scores 38 points.

86

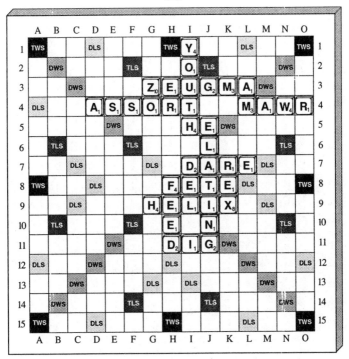

Your target score is 52

Can you find a play that scores exactly 52?
Can you find a play that scores just over 52?
The board includes the word ELATING.
Can you find its three anagrams?

Solution to Puzzle 84

PARADES at B4 down scores 78 points. PARTYING at D11 across
scores 42 points.

87

Your target score is 40

Can you find a play that scores exactly 40?
Can you find a play that scores just over 40?
What is the highest score you can get for
playing five tiles without using the E?

Solution to Puzzle 85

ZEUGMA at F2 down scores 44 points. GAZUMP at D10 across
scores 46 points. CAME at G11 down scores 36 points.

88

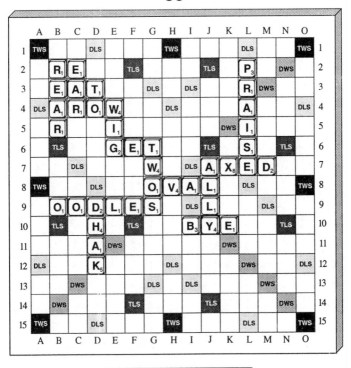

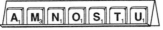

Your target score is 43

Can you find a play that scores exactly 43?
Can you find a seven-letter word from the above
tiles and find two places to play it on the board?

Solution to Puzzle 86

CARDIGANS at E11 across scores 52 points. CAFETERIAS at F8 across scores 56 points. The three anagrams of ELATING are ATINGLE, GELATIN and GENITAL.

89

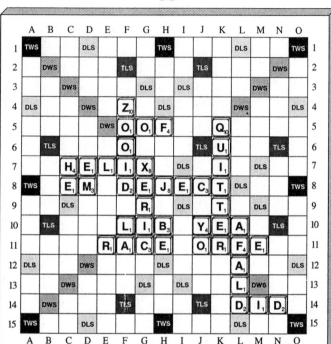

Your target score is 40

Can you find a play that scores exactly 40?
Can you play an eight-letter anagram with the above
tiles and using a letter on the board?

Solution to Puzzle 87
MONOCLE at F6 across scores 40 points. COLUMN at N10 down
scores 41 points. LOCUM at J14 across scores 34 points.

90

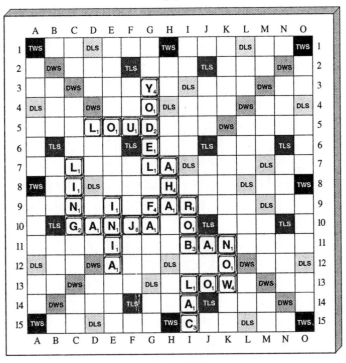

Your target score is 40

Can you find two plays that score exactly 40?
What is the highest score you can get
without using the K?

Solution to Puzzle 88

MANGETOUT at B6 across scores 43 points. AMOUNTS can be
played at I1 across for 90 points and at A5 down for 87 points. The
two other anagrams, OUTMANS and MOUTANS, are unplayable.

91

Your target score is 45

**Can you find a play which scores exactly 45?
Can you find a seven-letter word from the above
tiles and find two places to play it?**

Solution to Puzzle 89

SHEPHERD at C6 down scores 40 points. PERISHED at M5 down
scores 79 points.

92

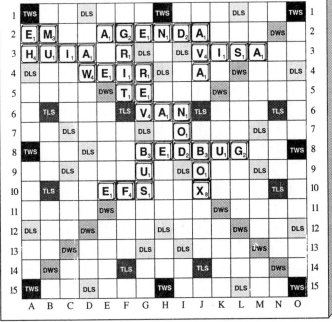

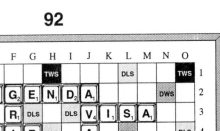

Your target score is 40

Can you find a play which scores exactly 40?
Can you find a play that scores just over 40?
What is the highest score you can get for
playing a word starting with the Y?

Solution to Puzzle 90

ATTACK at D10 down and KILOWATT at G13 across both score
40 points. TACTIC at G15 across scores 39 points.

93

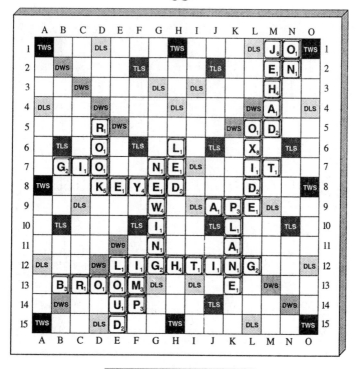

Your target score is 54

Can you find a play which scores exactly 54?
Can you find a play that scores just over 54?
What is the highest score you can get for playing
a word that goes through square H4?

Solution to Puzzle 91

TEETOTAL at E8 across scores 45 points. ATHLETE can be played
at N2 down for 81 points or at E14 across for 72 points.

94

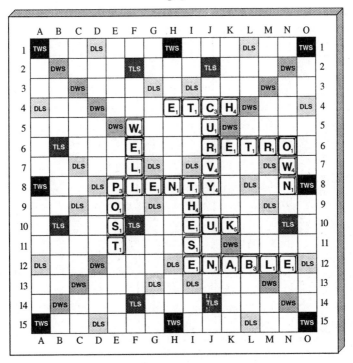

Can you find a seven-letter word from these
tiles that can be played on the above board?
In how many different places can the word be played?

Solution to Puzzle 92

AILED at H1 across scores 40 points. VANDALIZE at G6 across
scores 46 points. YIELD at J11 across scores 34 points.

95

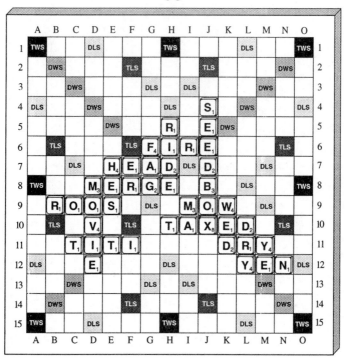

Your target score is 45

Can you find two plays that score exactly 45?
Can you find a play that scores just over 45?

Solution to Puzzle 93

MOONLIGHTING at A12 across scores 54 points. MONKEYED at A8 across scores 59 points. MONOCLED at H1 down scores 42 points.

96

	A	B	C	D	E	F	G	H	I	J	K	L	M	N	O	
1	TWS			DLS				TWS				DLS			TWS	1
2		DWS				TLS				TLS				DWS		2
3			G₂				DLS		DLS				DWS			3
4	DLS		R₁	DWS				DLS		J₈	DWS				DLS	4
5			U₁		DWS				D₂	O₁			R₁			5
6		TLS	F₄			TLS			I₁	T₁			A₁			6
7			E₁	M₃	U₁		DLS		DLS	V₄			DLS	N₁		7
8	TWS			A₁	G₂	O₁	N₁	I₁	Z₁₀	E₁		DLS		T₁	TWS	8
9			DLS	R₁			DLS		DLS	S₁	O₁	Y₄	A₁	S₁		9
10		TLS		S₁		TLS				TLS				TLS		10
11			O₁	H₄	M₃						DWS					11
12	DLS		B₃	Y₄	E₁			DLS				DWS			DLS	12
13			O₁		N₁	I₁	X₈		DLS				DWS			13
14		DWS	E₁			TLS				TLS				DWS		14
15	TWS			DLS			TWS					DLS			TWS	15
	A	B	C	D	E	F	G	H	I	J	K	L	M	N	O	

Your tiles: A   D₂   S₁   T₁   Q₁₀   U₁   W₄

Your target score is 38

Can you find a play that scores exactly 38?
Can you find a play that scores just over 38?

Solution to Puzzle 94

CRUSADE can be played at G3 across for 102 points, at O1 down
for 95 points, at O9 down for 93 points, at D4 down for 90 points, at
F13 across for 81 points and at B3 across for 76 points. Its
anagram SCAURED is unplayable.

97

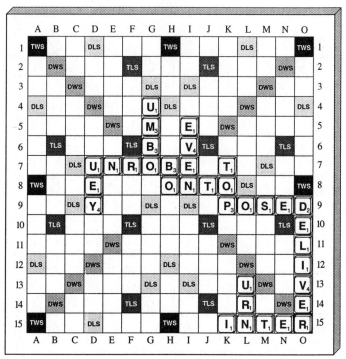

A | J₁ | J₈ | Q₁₀ | T₁ | U₁ | X₈ | Z₁₀

Your target score is 51

Can you find a play that scores exactly 51?
Can you find a play that scores just over 51?
What is the highest score you can get for
playing exactly two letters?

Solution to Puzzle 95

SUBMERGE at A8 across and BUSHFIRE at C6 across both score
45 points. HUSBANDRY at L4 down scores 47 points.

98

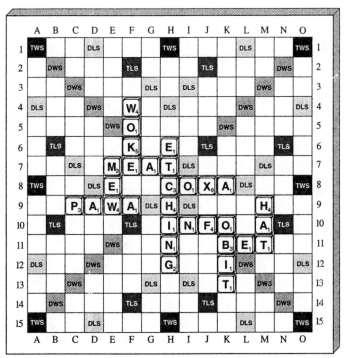

Your target score is 33

Can you find a play using the B that scores exactly 33?
Can you find a play, not using the B,
that scores just over 33?

Solution to Puzzle 96

QUADRANTS at N1 down scores 38 points. SAWDUST at D10
across scores 39 points.

99

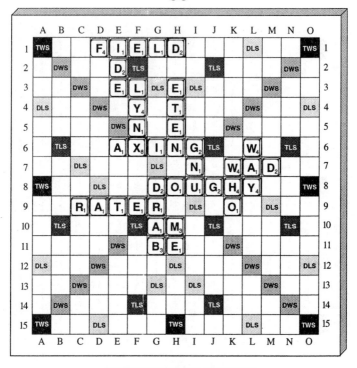

Your target score is 37

Can you find a play that scores exactly 37?
Can you find a play that scores just over 37?
What is the highest score you can get for playing
only three of your tiles?

Solution to Puzzle 97

QUAINTER at H15 across scores 51 points. JUXTAPOSED at F9
across scores 52 points. TOPAZ at K7 down scores 32 points.

100

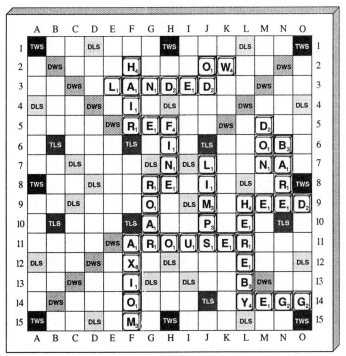

Your target score is 46

Can you find a play that scores exactly 46?
Can you find a play that scores just over 46?
Can you play only three tiles to score exactly 39
in two different places?

Solution to Puzzle 98

MEATBALL at E7 across scores 33 points. LLAMA at N7 down
scores 34 points.

Solution to Puzzle 99

WAYFARE at L6 down scores 37 points. GIVEAWAY at L1 down scores 40 points. AIRFIELD at A1 across scores 36 points.

Solution to Puzzle 100

REVIEWER at G8 across scores 46 points. CAREFREE at D5 across scores 52 points. REDEFINE at H1 down and ACE at E10 down both score 39 points.

Glossary

This glossary contains all the unusual words which appear in the preceding Scrabble puzzles, together with the puzzle number in which they appear.

ADZE   also spelt ADZ, this is a cutting tool with a curved blade **(64)**

AFALD   a Scottish word meaning single-minded or sincere; its alternative spellings are AEFALD, AEFAULD or AFAWLD **(89)**

AJWAN   a caraway plant, also spelt AJOWAN **(69)**

ALFA   another spelling of HALFA, a North African esparto grass **(83)**

ALOD   a short form of AL(L)ODIUM, and also spelt ALLOD, an estate of a feudal superior **(59)**

BATHMITZVAH   a Jewish girl attaining the age of religious responsibility. Alternative spellings include BASMITZVAH and BATMITZVAH **(20)**

CATE   an archaic word for a delicacy **(23)**

CHE   a dialectic pronoun. Its extension to CHEZ – at the home of – is worth knowing **(25)**

CHI   the Greek letter χ; its extension CHIK, another spelling of chick, and CHIV, slang for a knife, are useful **(23)**

CLY   an old slang word meaning to seize or steal. Hence the forms CLIES, CLIED and CLYING are allowed **(78)**

COBZA   a stringed folk instrument **(69)**

COXA   the hip bone **(98)**

COZ   a contraction of cousin **(27)**

DAH   another spelling of DA, a Burmese knife **(5)**

DAL   the Indian pigeon-pea, also spelt DHAL or DAHL, the latter being an extension of DAH worth knowing **(34)**

DHAK   an Indian tree with butterfly-like leaves **(88)**

DIXY   a military cooking-pail, also spelt DIXIE **(24)**

EDH   an old English letter, a barred D, used to represent the sound 'th'. Also spelt ETH **(87)**

EGAD   a mild oath and a useful extension of GAD **(16)**

ERIACH   the blood-fine paid by a murderer to his victim's family **(85)**

ETEN   an archaic word for a giant and a hook for TEN which is worth knowing. It can also be spelt ETTIN **(99)**

EUOI   an interjection expressing Bacchic frenzy **(25, 71)**

EQUID   any hoofed animal, and a valuable hook for QUID **(68)**

ETA   the Greek letter η; its extensions BETA (β) ZETA (ζ) and THETA (θ) are also Greek letters **(28)**

EUK   a dialectic word meaning to itch. It has several alternative spellings: EWK, YEUK, YOUK, YUCK and YUKE **(94)**

FOU   a Scottish word meaning either full or drunk; it is also a Scottish word for a bushel **(45)**

GANJA   another word for marijuana **(90)**

GHI   clarified butter, often made from Buffalo milk, which can also be spelt GHEE **(58)**

GIO   a gully or creek, also spelt GEO **(93)**

GJU   another spelling of GU, the Shetland violin, and worth knowing when JUG will not fit on the board! **(81)**

GLYPH   an ornamental channel or fluting **(6)**

GRUFE   an old spelling of GROOF, a Scottish word for the front of the body or face **(96)**

HAE   a Scottish form of have; HAEING is not allowed, however, but the extension to HAET, a whit, is useful **(10, 27)**

HITHE   a small haven or port **(49)**

HUIA   a New Zealand bird related to the starling – a potential extension of HUI, a Maori gathering **(92)**

HWYL   a word of Welsh origin for 'divine inspiration in oratory' **(63)**

IGAPO   a riverside forest, often flooded. It can also be spelt GAPO and this therefore takes an I as a prefix **(61)**

ILIUM   a bone fusing the ischium and pubis **(34)**

INIA   the plural of INIUM, a protuberance on the back of the skull **(90)**

JALAP   the root of a plant of the morning-glory genus (ipomoea, which is a useful vowel-heavy word in itself) **(34)**

JEHAD   a holy war or crusade, also spelt JIHAD **(93)**

JIAO   a Chinese monetary unit, equal to ten fen **(14, 77)**

JINNI   a class of spirits in Muslim theology, also spelt JINN, DJINNI, JINNEE or GENIE **(80)**

JOTA   a Spanish dance – a useful extension of JOT **(5)**

JOWAR   an Indian grass related to sugar-cane. Also spelt JOWARI which is a useful extension **(33)**

JUMAR   a mountaineering term for a clip which grips the rope when weight is applied. It is also a verb, so JUMARRED and JUMARRING are permitted **(3)**

KHUD   a hollow or ravine in India **(60)**

KUMQUAT   a Chinese variety of orange **(23)**

KVETCH   a Yiddish word meaning to complain or whine **(27)**

LEW   an alternative form of LEV, the monetary unit of Bulgaria; LEW can also mean lukewarm **(51)**

LUAU   a Hawaiian dish made of coconut and fish **(62)**

MAAR   in geology, a crater formed by a single explosion **(75)**

MANEH   a variant of MINA – the Greek weight, not the bird – and a useful hook for MANE **(55)**

MAWR   a word of Welsh origin meaning a big awkward girl **(86)**

MEL   a mainly pharmaceutical term for honey **(46)**

MYCORHIZA   a fungal mycelium found in plants. It can also be spelt with a double R **(8)**

MYOPE   a short-sighted person, from MYOPIA, short-sightedness, and MYOPIC, short-sighted **(57)**

NEF   an ornamental stand for a knife, often ship-shaped **(28)**

OLID   rank-smelling; a useful extension of LID to know **(67)**

ORFE   a golden-yellow fish, and an extension of ORF – a viral infection of sheep – which is worth knowing **(89)**

OSTEAL   resembling or relating to bones; thus STEAL can take an O as a prefix **(53)**

OUABAIN   a poisonous alkaloid – and a useful vowel-heavy word **(11)**

OPE   a poetical form of open; hence OPED and OPING are also allowed **(65)**

OYE   A Scottish word for a grandchild, another spelling of OY or OE. Its extensions to OYER and OYEZ are useful **(18)**

PAWA   the New Zealand name for the abalone, also spelt PAUA **(98)**

PAWKY   a Scottish word for drily humorous **(5)**

PEC   a colloquial term for the pectoral muscle. Its extension to PECH, a Scottish word meaning to pant, is useful **(33, 61)**

PEEWEE   another word for the peewit or lapwing **(50)**

PILI   a type of nut and also the plural of PILUS, a hair **(72)**

PIPI   a Brazilian tropical plant or an Australasian edible shellfish **(34)**

PST   an interjection used to attract someone's attention. Its alternative spelling PSST rarely appears as the S is so valuable in Scrabble **(6)**

PUTTI   the plural of PUTTO, a plump naked boy often seen in Baroque art **(58)**

PUY   a small volcanic cone **(80)**

QANAT   an underground tunnel for carrying irrigation water **(4, 28)**

QIBLA   the point towards which Muslims turn in prayer; also spelt KIBLAH **(32)**

QIS   the plural of QI, the Chinese life-force **(21)**

QUACKSALVING   an archaic word for practising medicine **(32)**

QUAG   a boggy place **(6)**

QUINOA   a South American goosefoot **(41)**

QUEP   an interjection expressing derision, normally spelt GUP **(70)**

QUIPO   an old Peruvian mnemonic device of knotted cords. This and its alternative spelling QUIPU are useful extensions of QUIP **(25)**

RAH   a short form of HURRAH **(58)**

RAX   a Scottish word for to stretch. RAXED and RAXING are also allowed and this is a useful extension for AX **(2?)**

REH   an efflorescence of sodium salts, and an important extension of both RE and EH **(46)**

RIA   a drowned valley **(55)**

SCAURED   a Scottish spelling of SCARED **(94)**

SEKT   a German sparkling wine **(66)**

SIJO   A Korean verse form **(52)**

SOWF   an old Scottish word meaning to whistle or hum softly. It can also be spelt SOWFF **(80)**

TAE   a Scottish form of to, toe or too **(19)**

TALAQ   an Islamic divorcee **(69)**

TEF   an Ethiopian cereal grass, also spelt TEFF **(28)**

THO   a Spenserian word for those or then **(25, 29)**

TITI both a small southern USA tree and a small long-tailed monkey from South America **(95)**

UEY   an Australian colloquial for a U-turn – an odd looking word but of value in Scrabble **(97)**

UHURU   a Swahili word for freedom **(31)**

UMBO   the central boss of a shield; it can be prefixed by several letters to make BUMBO, DUMBO, GUMBO, JUMBO and RUMBO **(97)**

URE   an obsolete word for a practice; an obsolete word for an extinct wild ox, or a monetary unit in the Hebrides! **(30)**

WAHOO   interestingly, two different plants; either the burning bush (an ornamental shrub) or a Californian buckthorn **(3)**

URSINE   of a bear, or bear-like, from URSA, the Latin name for a bear **(73)**

USQUEBAUGH   a Gaelic word for whisky, mentioned in *Tam O'Shanter* **(5)**

VATU   the monetary unit of Vannatu **(85)**

VOE   a bay or creek in the Hebrides **(22)**

WAE   a Scottish word for sorrowful **(29)**

WEX   an obsolete spelling of wax. Its forms WEXED and WEXING are permitted but WEXY is not **(9)**

WOX   an obsolete past participle of WAX **(35)**

WOP   offensive slang for a member of a Latin or Mediterranean race **(33)**

XEBEC   a small three-masted ship, also spelt ZEBEC **(43)**

XENIAL   relating to guests; from XENIUM – a present made to a guest or ambassador **(82)**

XERIC   dry or lacking in moisture **(89)**

XEROMA   a dry condition of the conjunctiva. Its plural is XEROMAS or XEROMATA **(76)**

XYSTI   the plural of XYSTUS, an open colonnade or tree-planted walk. XYST is also allowed – a variant of XYSTUS **(54)**

YAHOO   a boorish lout, derived from a name given by Swift in *Gulliver's Travels* to a class of brutish animals **(9)**

YAKOW   a cross between a yak and a cow **(84)**

YAMULKA   the skullcap worn by Jewish males, also spelt YARMULKA **(3)**

YEGG   an American word for a burglar. YEGGMAN is also a valid word **(100)**

YGO   a Spenserian past participle of go. Its alternative spelling of YGOE is a useful extension **(6)**

YOUNGTHLY   a Spenserian word for youthful **(12)**

YUPON   a bushy evergreen shrub, usually spelt YAUPON, and a useful hook for UPON **(91)**

ZAMIA   a palm-like tree or low shrub **(66)**

ZEBEC   another spelling of XEBEC **(79)**

ZEIN   a protein found in maize **(74)**

ZEUGMA   a figure of speech by which an adjective is applied to any two nouns **(85, 86)**

ZHO   another spelling of ZO, the Himalayan beast of burden. The other spellings, DSO, DZHO and DZO, are useful. The female is ZHOMO, DSOMO or JOMO and the male is ZOBO, ZOBU or DSOBO. All will be familiar to readers fluent in Tibetan! **(9, 47)**

ZIMOCCA   a type of bath sponge **(12)**

ZONAE   the plural of ZONA, a belt or girdle **(66)**

ZOOEA   the larval stage of certain crustaceans, also spelt ZOEA **(47)**

ZOOID   an organic cell capable of independent movement **(89)**

ZYMIC   the adjective from ZYME, a ferment **(10)**

Competitive Scrabble

A list of Scrabble clubs in Britain and organisations in English-speaking countries is available on the Internet at www.mattelscrabble.com or by post from Scrabble Clubs UK, Mattel House, Vanwall Business Park, Vanwall Road, Maidenhead, Berks SL6 4LB; tel: (01628) 500283; fax: (01628) 500288; email: nelkonph@mattel.com.

The clubs in the USA are available by state on the Internet at www.teleport.com/~stevena/scrabble. Or you can write to Joe Edley, National Scrabble Association, c/o Williams & Company, 120 Front Street Garden, Box 700, Greenport, NY 11944, USA. Tel: (516) 477 0033. Fax: (516) 477 0294. Email: info@Scrabble-assoc.com.

For British players, Gareth Williams, Association of Premier Scrabble Players, 209 Fidlas Road, Llanishen, Cardiff, South Glamorgan CF4 5NA, tel: (01222) 758249, produces a Newsletter with information on tournaments. Postal Scrabble in Britain is organised by Ms Muriel Patterson, Postal Scrabble Secretary, 5 Blenheim Close, Essex SS5 5AX.

World Champions

There have been four World Championships so far, and a fifth is planned for November 1999 at the Carlton Crest Hotel in Melbourne. All have been held under the auspices of J W Spear & Sons plc, now part of Mattel. The World Championship uses a combined dictionary which incorporates all words in *Official Scrabble Words* and the *Official Scrabble Player's Dictionary*.

Winners to date:

1991	London	**Peter Morris** (USA)
1993	New York	**Mark Nyman** (UK)
1995	London	**David Boys** (Canada)
1997	Washington	**Joel Sherman** (USA)

The Internet

There are many sites devoted to Scrabble on the Internet. Searching for Scrabble using a search engine, such as Hotbot, Lycos or Yahoo, will unearth most of them. The two official sites of the owners of the Scrabble trademark worldwide are at www.mattelscrabble.com for people outside North America and at www.hasbroscrabble.com for North American residents. There are links from these sites to all officially approved sites using the Scrabble trademark under licence. There are many other "pirate" sites using the Scrabble name and both Mattel and Hasbro have understandably threatened legal action against such sites from time to time.

Online Scrabble

The site at www.ozemail.com.au/~aspa provides online Scrabble where you can play against other people from all over the world. The problems with Scrabble on the Internet are twofold. Unlike chess, backgammon and bridge which have thriving servers, Scrabble requires one to obtain a license to run a server and to replicate the board and tiles, whichever version of the two almost identical sets is used. Furthermore the dictionary used for playing Scrabble is different in North America, which uses the *Official Scrabble Player's Dictionary*, and the UK and many other English speaking countries which use *Official Scrabble Words.* The world championships are held using a combined dictionary but copyright problems have prevented the distribution of such a book worldwide.The site at www.ozemail.com.au/~/rjackman provides competitions using a combined dictionary known as SOWPODS.

Computer Programs and Reference Material

Perhaps the best source of information on computer programs is the site at www.telport.com/~stevena/scrabble/faq.html which has an excellent FAQ (Frequently Asked Questions) page which lists all the software and reference material available on Scrabble together with a number of rare publications. The Scrabble Player, available from Eidos Interactive on (44) 11 356 0831, is one of the best Scrabble playing programs on the market. In the US and Canada this is known as CrossWise and is available from Cygnus Cybernetics Corporation on (800) 357 8768.

Bibliography

There are a number of reference books which are essential for the serious Scrabble player. All reference books for Scrabble are published by Chambers Harrap:

The Chambers Dictionary   300,000 definitions of all words which are allowed in Scrabble

Official Scrabble Words , *3rd Edition*   This contains all words of two to nine letters and their inflexions which are allowed in Scrabble and is essential to resolve disputes on 'er' forms of verbs and adjectives

Official Scrabble Lists   An invaluable aid to the Scrabble player wishing to improve his skill by learning high-scoring words, anagrams, hooks, and letter combinations

Scrabble for Beginners by Barry Grossman. A good starting point for someone wanting to learn the game from scratch

World Championship Scrabble by Gyles Brandreth and Darryl Francis.   22 games from the 1991 World Championship

The Ultimate Scrabble Book by Philip Nelkon. Tips on tactics for tournaments. Quizzes and puzzles (this title is published by Stanley Paul).

The Scrabble magazine *Onwords* is edited by co-author Allan Simmons and is published four times per year. For a subscription, send £6 (£10 overseas) for six issues to Onwords, Shilling House, 1 Woolmer Hill, Haslemere, Surrey GU27 1LT. Tel: (01428) 643461